Divine Comedy

Spiritual Musings & Hysterical Religious Cartoons Vol. 2

Dan Reynolds

Joseph Weiss, Editor

ISBN-13: 978-1-943760-95-4 (Color Print)
ISBN-13: 978-1-943760-96-1 (e-Book)

FOREWORD

The book you are holding (Divine Comedy Volume 2) is part of a collection of faith- based cartoons I call DIVINE COMEDY. My use of religious cartoons is to remind people of how important humor is in our lives, especially our faith lives. Humor enhances perspective, and helps us weigh and balance life's trials and tribulations. I like to think God gave us all a mouth whose smile lifts up, toward Heaven.

I also go around near and far doing what I call a DIVINE COMEDY presentation on how humor and joy can enrich one's faith life. It is filled with hysterical religious cartoons, commentary, jokes, and woven together with a serious message about the importance of Christian joy. To invite me to your parish, school, group, or conference, and to learn more about having this fun, informative, and memorable presentation, please contact him me at:

divinecomedydan@gmail.com

Also, visit me at DIVINE COMEDY website at:

DivineComedyDan.weebly.com

I think a positive way to encourage more people to say a "novena", is start calling it a "yesvena".

t. Patrick Drives the Snakes Out of Ireland...

Some say, "There's no time like the present." I say there's no present like time.

"Can I get a stripper here?"

Angels are the messengers of God. So are evANGELists.

This message is written in a special type of invisible ink. Only sinners can read it.

Talk is cheap... listening priceless.

Every time a bell rings, an angel gets his wings.

'Marriage' is between one man and one woman. Anything else is a 'mirage'.

Avoiding Truth is like running away from your own shadow.

The First and Last Male-Sponsored
Baby Shower

If our eyes are the windows of the soul, then we must be the "pupils" of the Holy Spirit.

"Do you have any oranges?"

Real love is not a feeling.
Feelings change.
Love is a decision that
always remains.

"I gotta bad feeling about these apples."

Our souls were made to perfectly reflect our Creator, and the fewer ripples we have the more we mirror His Image.

Adam & Eve: The Later Years...

"HELP! We've FALLEN...and we can't get up!"

"Unconditional love" begins with "U".

When the Enemy tells us
how useless we are,
we should consider
the source and take it as a
real compliment.

THE ETERNAL CONSEQUENCE FOR MEN NOT PUTTING THE SEAT DOWN...

It may be a toss-up as to
what hurts more deeply
.....what is said or
what is left unsaid.

It's not a coincidence that "Mother" consists mostly of "other".

Don't be hypocritical...
Hippos don't like it when
we criticize them.

There is nothing new under the sun, but everything is made new by the Son.

Happiness is a sunny day.
Joy is the weather itself.

Recipe For Success:
L-aughter
O-penness
V-irtue
E-mpathy

39

May 7th is the National Day of Prayer. So should May 8th, May 9th, May 10th, and every day be.

We must "b-less" in order to be more.

Let us focus not on the "us" part, but on the whole "Jes"us". We are "us"eless without Him.

Christmas reminds us that no matter how small a person is they can change the world.

Billy Graham as a kid.

Someone said, "If you love someone, don't be afraid to let them go." If you are a mountain climber, these words can be a little disconcerting.

False humility is like tickling yourself. You receive no effect from it, and no one else is laughing either.

Love is like baseball.
It begins at home, and its
goal is to return Home.

Don't worry about being a one-of-a-kind. Just try to be a kind one.

Why Priests Who Forget To Take Off Their Clip-On Mics Shouldn't Do Confessions Right After Mass.

Whenever you feel like
you've lost God,
start looking for Him
in the last place
He had you.

The true measure of love
is immeasurable.

Joy is the SONrise
of the heart.

How do we know God has a sense of humor? Because he often works in "hilarious" ways.

WHERE 'PASTOR'-IZED MILK COMES FROM...

We "raise" children because we are supposed to lift them up... to God.

Humor makes "You More".

When I was a kid, I used to wonder why people were trading items for their bellybutton lint every year. I'd always hear people say to each other just before Ash Wednesday..."And what are you giving up for lint."

Moses' first and last day as a lifeguard.

I hope someday they will say about me...In the great quilt of Life he never fell to pieces because he was such a stitch.

I read a good quote about the importance of knowing yourself. It was written by someone named "Anonymous".

AS A CHILD, HE WAS KNOWN AS
JUDAS ASPARAGUS

Proof that laughter is good for you...have you ever seen a hyena in therapy?

75

Then there was the anniversary that I thought God told me in prayer that He had a plant for my wife so I didn't buy her a present. Turns out what God actually said was that He had a plan for my life. Obviously, the plan didn't involve listening very well.

"Do you really need a Pat on the back for everything?"

The Fruit of God's love died on the wood of the cross, and the seeds of Mercy were scattered onto the soil of Faith which grew into the Church.

Inside every "pr**aye**r",
there is an "aye" or
a "yes" to God.

IRISH EYES BEGAN SMILING ON MARCH 17, 461... THE DAY ST. PATRICK DISCOVERED IRISH CREAM.

When you lose a faithful friend on earth, you gain a faithful friend in Heaven.

The Law becomes Love, when man realizes he doesn't have to...he gets to.

ST. PATRICK DRIVES THE STEAKS OUT OF IRELAND

In the end when it's all said and done, it's better to have said less and done more.

"Now do you know what 'No L' means?"

As we age, God provides us
with a natural facelift.
It's called a smile.

When I was a kid, one year
for Lent, I gave up Lent.

God is proof that He exists.

93

Left-handers are Gods way of reminding us that all is not right with the world.

95

A picture is worth a thousand words, but reality will leave you speechless.

Facebook often reminds me why God did not give us the ability to know what others are thinking.

"But, LORD, aren't these tablets a graven image?"

"Abortion" sounds like "abhor" & "shun". Coincidence? I think not.

A man's got to do what a man's got to do, and if he forgets, a woman has to do what a woman has to do, and remind him.

During Paul Revere's famous "Midnight Ride", he may have been describing the animals on Noah's Ark when he said, "One if by land, two if by sea."

Yankee fans think the Bible starts with the Book of Ruth because the Bible begins with "In the big inning."

"Go ahead, honey. Put your hands in the hands of the man who stills the water."

Life is not a multiple choice test. There is only just one answer. If you know the answer - Jesus, you will never fail.

I got a real tough penance from the priest. He told me to do a decade of the rosary. The good news is I only have one more year to go.

God doesn't make mistakes, this is true. He makes all things good. That's why He made you.

If faith were just based on feelings, you could have a spiritual awakening with just a cup of coffee.

"We found the eternal flames a bit too cushy. So, we did a little upgrade."

God is found in silence. The devil hides in cacophony. When you go to church for entertain**me**nt, guess who it's all about?
You know why you should really **go d**on't you?

A reading from the Letter of Paul to the Galoshes...
Stupid Galoshes!
Reynolds

We're sort of like a misplaced shoe. God keeps searching us out so we don't become a lost "sole".

A reminder of the True Presence of Christ in the Eucharist... Eu**CH**a**RIST.**

Dan Reynolds

Dan was born and raised a cradle Catholic in Oswego, NY. He attended Bishop Cunningham Catholic High School in Oswego, NY, graduated from SUNY Oswego with a degree in Psychology, spent 4 years in the Navy on the USS NIMITZ aircraft carrier traveling to many places in the world while working with the Navy Chaplains aboard the ship. He worked 22 years at the Oswego City County Youth Bureau as the Youth Activities Coordinator.

For the past 27 years, Dan has been a professional cartoonist. His cartoon work is distributed nationally via National Greeting card companies like American Greetings. His greeting card work can be found in every city in the country via outlets like Wal-Mart, Target, and many other chain stores. His work has also appeared in magazines like Reader's Digest, and Harvard Business Review, Boy's Life, Catholic Digest, and many others. Beginning in September of 2017, Dan's work will begin appearing in every issue of Catholic Digest. He has 4 nationally published books with Andrews McMeel Publishing, the publishers of Calvin and Hobbes and The Far Side.

His Reader's Digest artwork in a 4-month exhibit in 2011 at the Everson Museum in Syracuse, NY. His cartoon work also appeared once on an opening season episode of THE SOPRANOS, and on the Discovery's Science Channel. Two of his greeting cards won nominations for a LOUIE award. A LOUIE AWARD is the equivalent of the movie academy award nomination only in the greeting card industry.

Dan is a cancer survivor which he battled in 2008 and 2009, receiving chemo treatments along operations.

Currently, Dan is going into his second year of diaconate training for the Diocese of Syracuse, NY, having first completed the required preliminary 2 years of Formation for Ministry. God willing, Dan will be ordained a deacon in 2020.

When he's not cartooning, Dan's spends about 20 hours a week as the Coordinator of Parish Life at Divine Mercy Parish in Central Square, NY. And travels to share his apostolate THE DIVINE COMEDY presentation, hoping to spread the joy of the Gospel message.

And most importantly, Dan is married, and has 4 sons, (2 of which presently attend Franciscan University in Steubenville, Ohio), and lives in Brewerton, NY.

Dan's Divine Comedy website
and e-mail address is:
divinecomedydan@gmail.com
www.divinecomedydan.weebly.com

Sign-up for Dan's daily REYNOLDS
UNWRAPPED e-mail cartoon for only $12
for a whole year. E-mail Dan at
reynoldsunwrapped@gmail.com for
details. Dan's website is:
www.reynoldsunwrapped.weebly.com

The Funny Side Collection is available at:
www.thefunnysidecollection.com
www.smartaskbooks.com

CPSIA information can be obtained
at www.ICGtesting.com
Printed in the USA
BVHW011826141222
654254BV00029BA/740